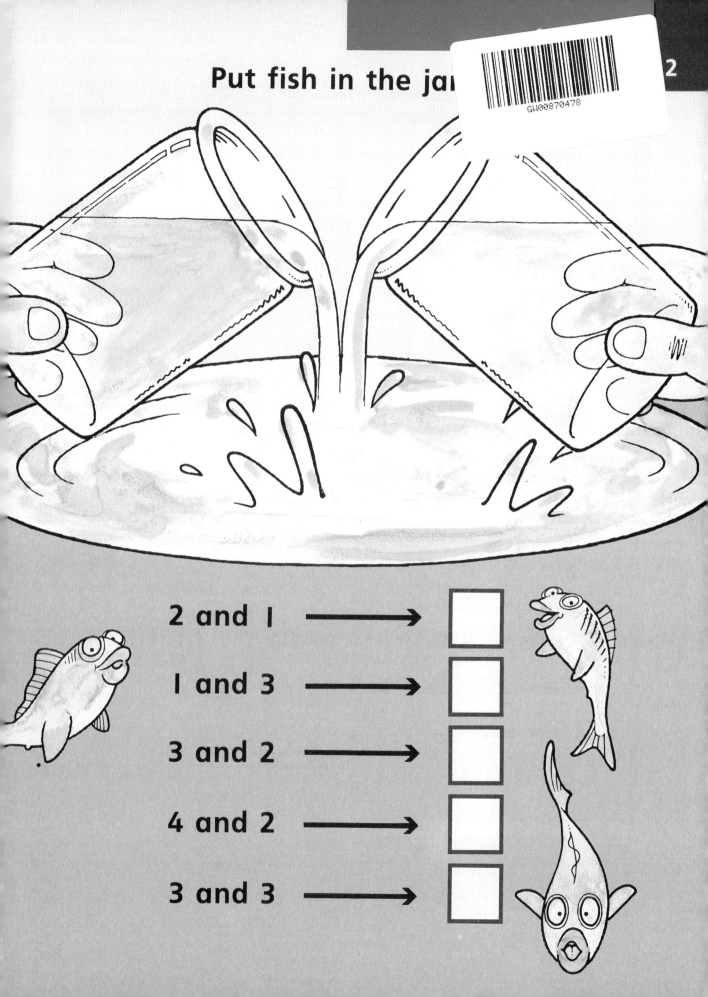

Put fish in the jar

2

2 and 1 ⟶ ☐

1 and 3 ⟶ ☐

3 and 2 ⟶ ☐

4 and 2 ⟶ ☐

3 and 3 ⟶ ☐

Girls and boys

Put in

| 5 girls | 2 boys | → | ☐ altogether |

| 5 girls | 5 boys | → | ☐ altogether |

| 3 girls | 6 boys | → | ☐ altogether |

| 2 girls | 6 boys | → | ☐ altogether |

SPMG

HEINEMANN MATHEMATICS 1

Name

WORKBOOK 5
Addition to 6

Revised

I

How many fish?

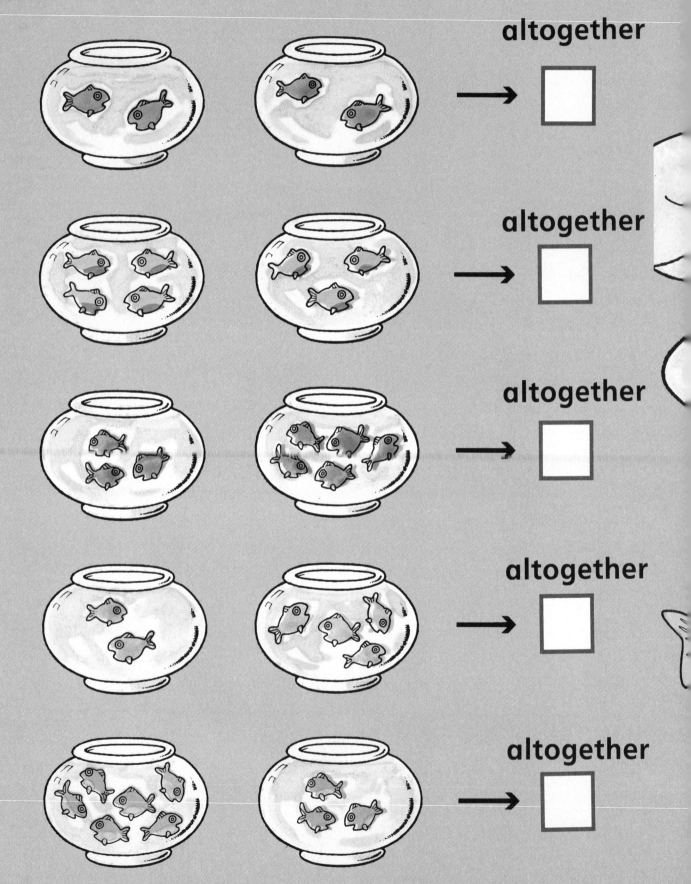

altogether

altogether

altogether

altogether

altogether

Girls and boys

3 and 3 →

and →

and →

and →

and →

and →

Draw and add.

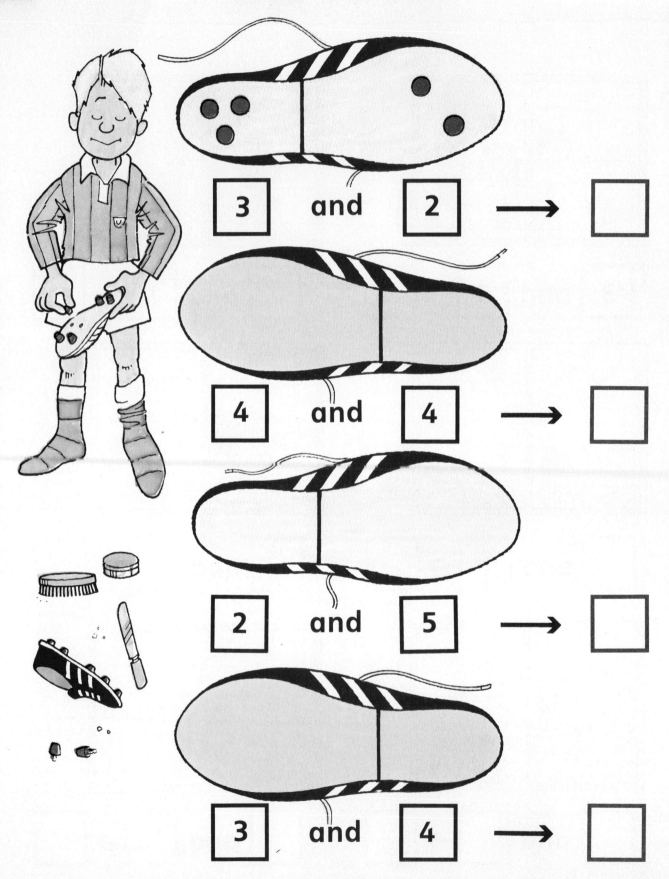

3 and 2 →

4 and 4 →

2 and 5 →

3 and 4 →

How many altogether?

___4___ **and** ___2___ **more** ➝ ☐

___2___ **and** _____ **more** ➝ ☐

_____ **and** _____ **more** ➝ ☐

_____ **and** _____ **more** ➝ ☐

Peas

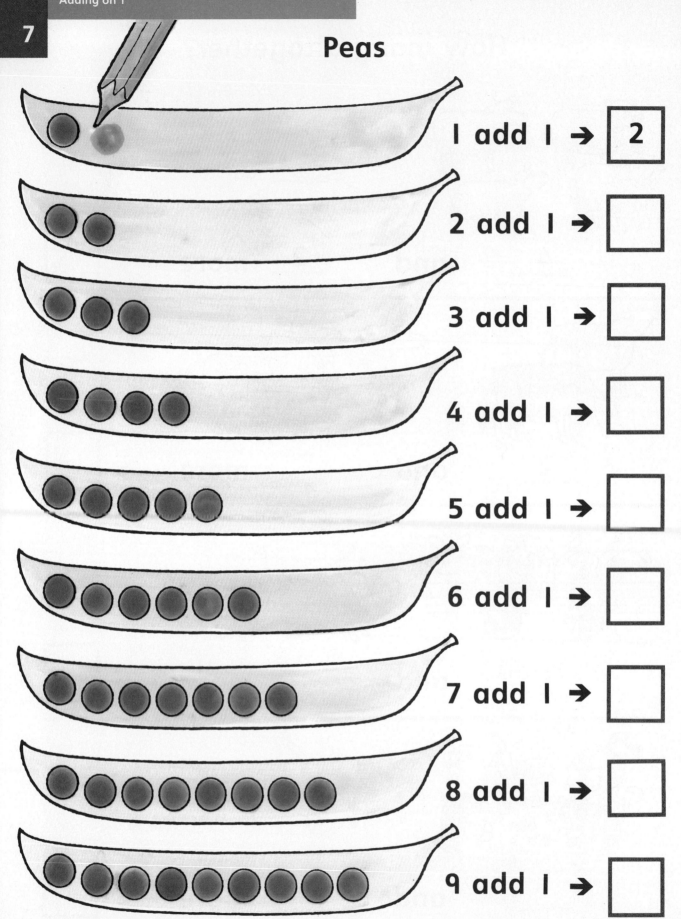

1 add 1 → 2

2 add 1 →

3 add 1 →

4 add 1 →

5 add 1 →

6 add 1 →

7 add 1 →

8 add 1 →

9 add 1 →

Ice cubes

Put in 6 ⬜ .
Add 2.

6 add 2 → ☐

Put in 3 ⬜ .
Add 2.

3 add 2 → ☐

1 add 2 ⟶ ☐   5 add 2 ⟶ ☐

2 add 2 ⟶ ☐   6 add 2 ⟶ ☐

3 add 2 ⟶ ☐   7 add 2 ⟶ ☐

4 add 2 ⟶ ☐   8 add 2 ⟶ ☐

R1

Adding 1 or 2

| 1 | add | 1 | → | |

| 3 | add | 2 | → | |

| 4 | + | 1 | → | |

| 1 | + | | → | |

| | + | | → | |

| | + | | → | |

Adding 1 or 2

3   **+**   **1**   →   ☐

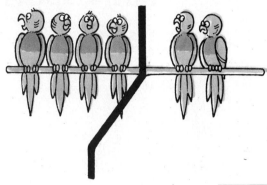

4   **+**   **2**   →   ☐

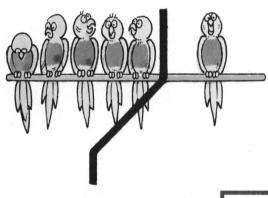

5   **+**   **1**   **=**   ☐

2   **+**   ☐   **=**   ☐

☐   **+**   ☐   **=**   ☐

☐   **+**   ☐   **=**   ☐

Use 4 counters.

Put 4 spots on the monster.

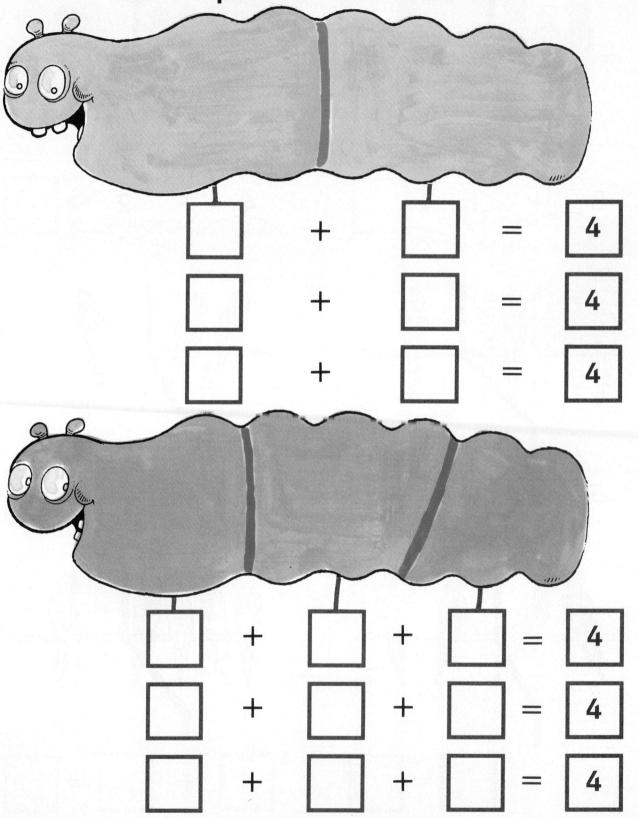

$$\square + \square = 4$$

$$\square + \square = 4$$

$$\square + \square = 4$$

$$\square + \square + \square = 4$$

$$\square + \square + \square = 4$$

$$\square + \square + \square = 4$$

Draw spots.

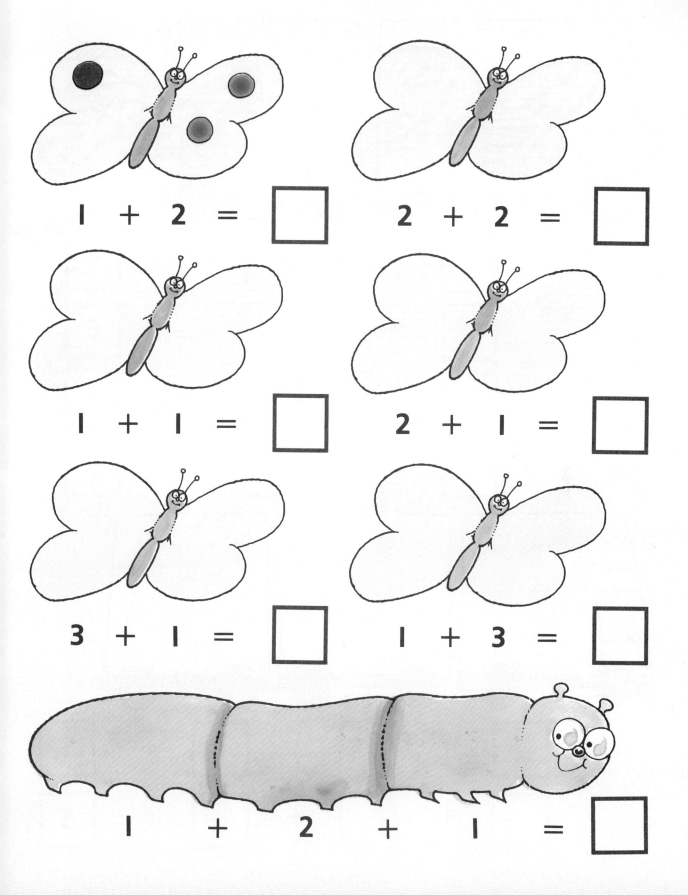

1 + 2 = ☐

2 + 2 = ☐

1 + 1 = ☐

2 + 1 = ☐

3 + 1 = ☐

1 + 3 = ☐

1 + 2 + 1 = ☐

Put in 5 parcels.

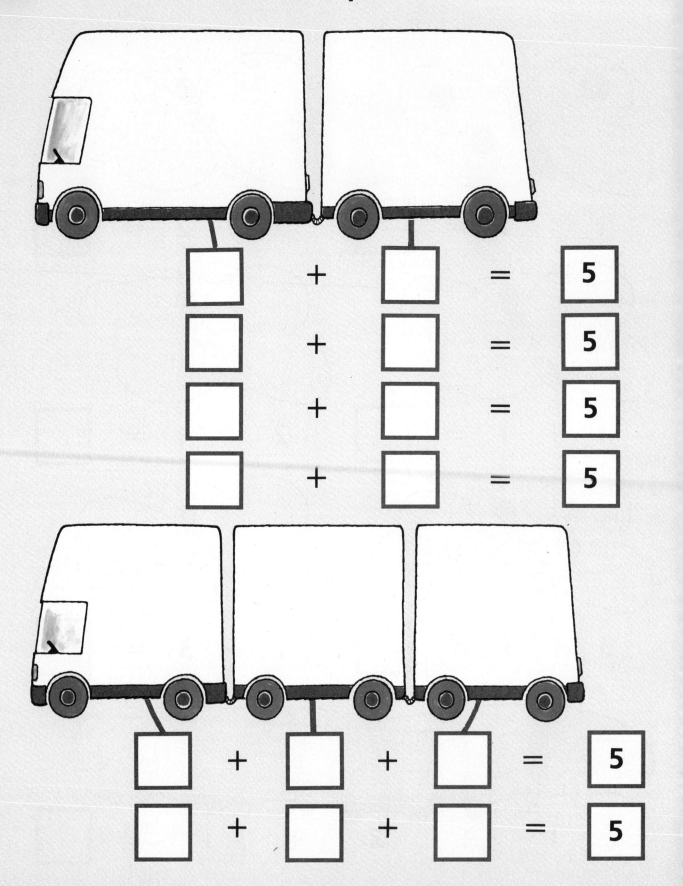

Draw and add.

3 + 1 = ☐

4 + 1 = ☐

3 + 2 = ☐

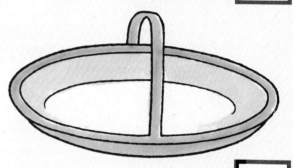

2 + 3 = ☐

2 + 2 = ☐

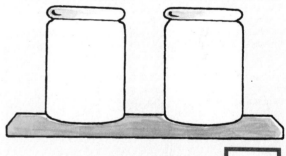

1 + 4 = ☐

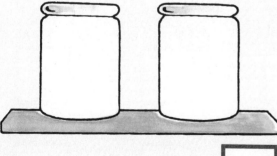

1 + 3 = ☐

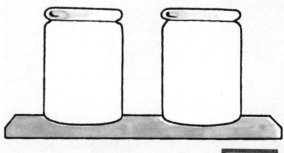

2 + 3 = ☐

R2

Count and add.

$$1 + 4 = \boxed{}$$

$$\boxed{} + \boxed{} = \boxed{}$$

$$\boxed{} + \boxed{} = \boxed{}$$

$$\boxed{} + \boxed{} = \boxed{}$$

$$\boxed{} + \boxed{} = \boxed{}$$

$$\boxed{} + \boxed{} + \boxed{} = \boxed{}$$

Spots

Monday

$$1 + 5 = 6$$

Tuesday

$$2 + 4 =$$

Wednesday

$$3 +$$

Thursday

Friday

Saturday

R3

Moves

Start here

1 2 3

Move  and ▢ ⟶ ▢

Move and ⟶ ▢

Move and ⟶ ▢

Move and ⟶ ▢

Move and ⟶ ▢

Move and ⟶ ▢

4 + 1 =

Draw dots.

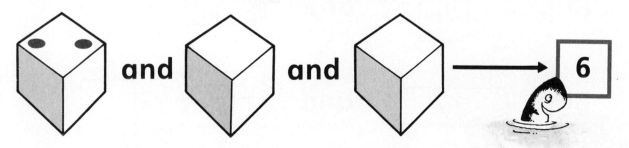

and ... and ... → 6

Sam's Sw

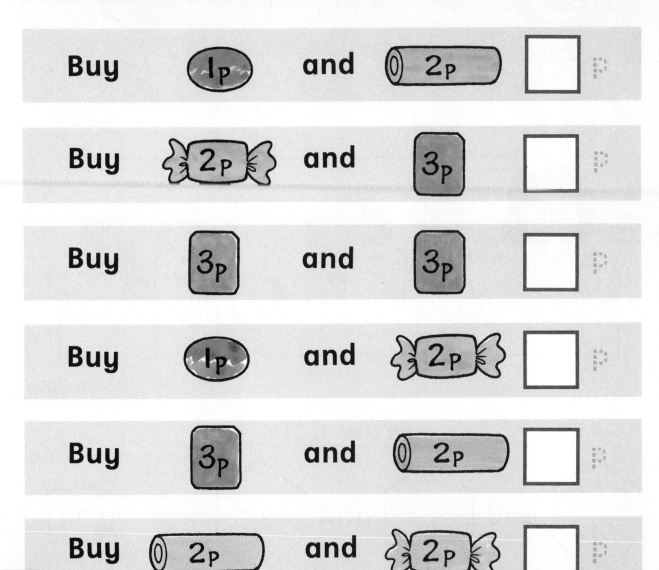

Buy 1p and 2p ☐

Buy 2p and 3p ☐

Buy 3p and 3p ☐

Buy 1p and 2p ☐

Buy 3p and 2p ☐

Buy 2p and 2p ☐

et Shop

Make each 1p more.

Make each 2p more.

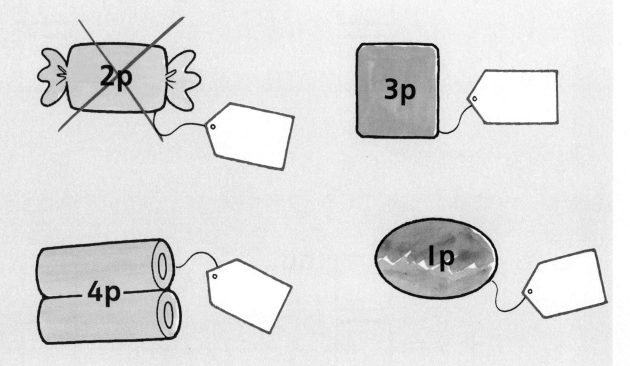

Pets

$2 + 1 = $ ☐

$1 + 2 = $ ☐

$3 + 1 = $ ☐

$1 + 3 = $ ☐

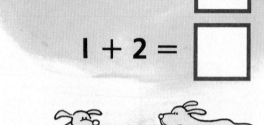

$4 + 1 = $ ☐

$1 + 4 = $ ☐

$3 + 2 = $ ☐

$2 + 3 = $ ☐

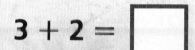

$5 + 1 = $ ☐

$1 + 5 = $ ☐

$4 + 2 = $ ☐

$2 + 4 = $ ☐

How many?

on the bridge ☐

under the bridge ☐

altogether ☐

on the branch ☐

under the branch ☐

altogether ☐

on the rope ☐

under the rope ☐

altogether ☐

on the desk ☐

under the desk ☐

altogether ☐

Fish

Write number stories   🐟 2 + 3 = 5

🐟		⭐	
🐟		🐟	
🦀		🐙	

1	2	3	4	5	6	7	8	9	10	11	12	13	14	15	16	17	18	19	20	21	22	23

Published by Heinemann Educational Publishers, Halley Court, Jordan Hill, Oxford OX2 8EJ,
a division of Reed Educational and Professional Publishers Ltd.
ISBN 0 435 03705 6 © Scottish Primary Mathematics Group 1991.
First published 1991. Revised edition 1995.   96 97 98 99   7 6 5 4 3 2
Typeset and Illustrated by Oxprint Design. Printed by Jarrold Printing, Norwich.

ISBN 0-435-03086-8